English
SKETCHES
and studies

September 25 – October 12
Monday to Friday 10–6.30

London

ANTHONY REED
First floor, 3 Cork Street, W.1

November 7 – 25
Tuesday to Saturday 10–5

New York

DAVIS & LONG COMPANY
746 Madison Avenue, NY 10021

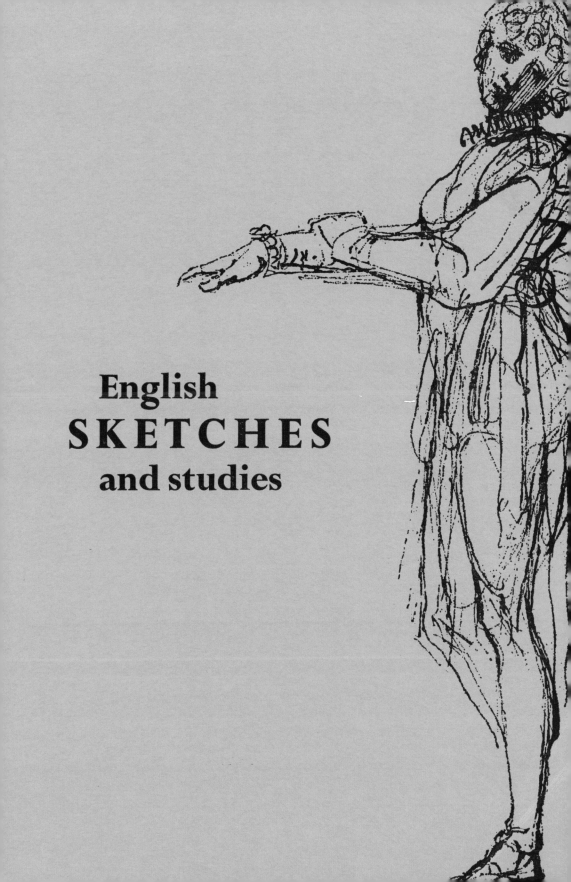

English
SKETCHES
and studies

ILLUSTRATIONS

FRONT COVER: Two sketches of a girl dancing, with cymbals – by George Romney, catalogue number 13

INSIDE FRONT COVER: Diana and her nymphs bathing in a woodland pool – by William Taverner, catalogue number 5

INSIDE BACK COVER: View from Porchester Terrace, Bayswater – by John Varley, catalogue number 42

TITLE PAGE AND THIS PAGE: Details from a sheet of figure studies – by John Henry Fuseli, R.A., catalogue number 22

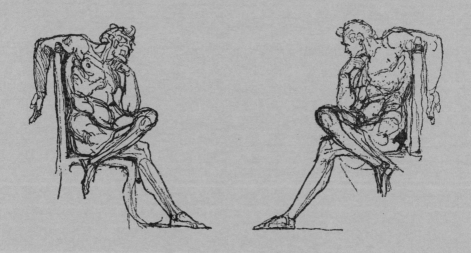

VIOLA *martia multiplici flore.* 3. *pin.*

FRANCIS LE PIPER   died 1695

1   *Six grotesque heads*

Pen and grey ink, with grey wash, each drawing circular, 1⅛ inches in diameter

Le Piper was an amateur artist of Walloon descent, well educated, widely travelled and, according to a contemporary account, 'of facetious humour'. Much of his life appears to have been spent sketching and making caricatures in the taverns of Bermondsey. Little of his work has survived. Only eight other drawings have previously been recorded. Four are in the British Museum and the remainder at Yale.

GEORG DIONYSIUS EHRET   1708–1770

2   *A viola plant*   *Illustrated*

Watercolour and bodycolour on vellum, 7⅞ × 6½ inches
Signed and dated 1765. Inscribed 'Viola martia multiplici flore. B. pin.'
Provenance: John Ireland Blackburne (1783–1873)

PETER TILLEMANS   1684–1734

3   *A boy with his dog and other travellers in a sunken country lane below a gabled house*

Pencil, grey wash, watercolour and bodycolour, 6¾ × 8¾ inches
Provenance: William, 4th Lord Byron

Lord Byron, to whom this drawing was formerly attributed, was a patron of Tillemans and probably also his pupil. Their respective levels of accomplishment in drawing may be studied in the Print Room at the British Museum, and are also exemplified on a double-sided sheet in the Oppe collection, with a signed Tillemans on one side and a signed Byron on the other.

4   *A sportsman seated beneath a tree in a hilly landscape, watching horsemen and hounds passing through a valley*

Pencil and watercolour, 3⅞ × 6½ inches

WILLIAM TAVERNER   1703–1772

5   *Diana and her nymphs bathing in a woodland pool*

Pencil and red chalk, with grey wash and watercolour, $7\frac{1}{2} \times 12\frac{1}{4}$ inches
Provenance: John Thane, The Hon. Lady Inglis

Thane, whose name is inscribed twice on the drawing – in full at bottom centre, and abbreviated to J.Th. on the right margin – was a well-known 18th century collector with a particular interest in Gainsborough drawings.

THOMAS GAINSBOROUGH, R.A.   1727–1788

6   *Paling at the edge of a thicket, with open parkland to the right*

Pencil, $5\frac{3}{4} \times 7\frac{3}{8}$ inches
Provenance: Monro family

Drawn about 1750

7   *A cottage in woodland at sunset*   *Illustrated*

Watercolour and bodycolour, $9\frac{3}{4} \times 7\frac{1}{2}$ inches

Painted about 1765.

THOMAS GAINSBOROUGH, R.A. 1727–1788

8 *Woodland landscape with distant windmill* *Illustrated*

Black and white chalks on blue-grey paper, $10\frac{5}{8} \times 12\frac{7}{8}$ inches
Provenance: H. B. Milling, Mrs. W. W. Spooner
Literature: Dr. John Hayes, 'The drawings of Thomas Gainsborough', Zwemmer 1970, page 201, catalogue number 398

Drawn about 1778.

GIOVANNI BATTISTA CIPRIANI, R.A. 1727–1775

9 *Design for an allegorical painting, possibly an overdoor*

Pen and ink, with watercolour, $4 \times 12\frac{1}{4}$ inches
Provenance: Benjamin West, P.R.A., from whose estate it was bought in 1820 by William Esdaile. The mount bears Esdaile's initials

PAUL SANDBY, R.A.   1725–1809

10   *The Duke of Cumberland with a gentleman and a groom, all*
mounted, and dogs   *Illustrated*

Pencil and watercolour, $5\frac{1}{2} \times 8\frac{3}{8}$ inches

This is a study for the principal figures in the watercolour of this subject in the collection
of Her Majesty the Queen. The drawing was acquired for the Royal collection at Windsor
in 1946 and, like this study, it had at one time been attributed to John Wootton.
The Duke of Cumberland, who is depicted reviewing his string of racehorses at exercise,
retired to Windsor after his military career had ended with the Seven Years War. The stud
which he founded was brilliantly successful, its progeny including the great Eclipse.

11   *A thistle*   *Illustrated*

Pen and ink, with watercolour, $5\frac{3}{8} \times 5\frac{3}{4}$ inches
Signed, or inscribed with the artist's name

SAWREY GILPIN, R.A.   1733–1807

12   *Donkeys*

Pencil, pen and ink, and watercolour, $6\frac{1}{2} \times 9\frac{7}{8}$ inches
Signed

GEORGE ROMNEY   1734–1802

13   *Two sketches of a girl dancing, with cymbals*

Pen and brown ink, $6\frac{7}{8} \times 5\frac{1}{4}$ inches
On the back: a slight sketch in pen and ink of a crouching figure

14   *Storm clouds over low hills*   *Illustrated*

Watercolour, $7\frac{1}{8} \times 10\frac{1}{2}$ inches
Provenance: Alfred de Pass, the Royal Institution of Cornwall at Truro, Richard
Hodgkin

This and the following two drawings are pages which have been extracted from a Romney
sketchbook and mounted for display. The pages have not been cut and the sketchbook may
be reassembled. The three drawings are offered for sale collectively, together with the
remaining pages of the sketchbook and its marbled paper cover. Few Romney sketchbooks
remain intact and no other landscape sketches in watercolour by the artist are known.

15   *A group of four trees beside a cart track on sloping ground*   *Illustrated*

Watercolour, $7\frac{1}{8} \times 10\frac{1}{2}$ inches
Provenance: as for catalogue number 14

See note on catalogue number 14.

16   *A lake, with gently rising ground beyond, and a clump of trees on the*
           skyline   *Illustrated*

Watercolour, $7\frac{1}{8} \times 10\frac{1}{2}$ inches
Provenance: as for catalogue number 14

See note on catalogue number 14.

FRANCIS TOWNE 1740–1816

17 *Llyn Cwellyn, near Snowdon*   *Illustrated*

Pen and grey ink, with watercolour, 10¾ × 16¾ inches
Signed, dated 1777 and numbered 28
Inscribed on the back 'No. 28 July 11, 1777 / View of Llyngwellyn / Drawn on the spot by Francis Towne / Light from the left hand'
Provenance: the Merivale family, Victor Rienaecker and Walter Hetherington
Exhibited: 'Original drawings by Francis Towne', at The Gallery, 20 Lower Brook Street, London, 1805, catalogue number 32
Literature: Adrian Bury, 'Francis Towne', Charles Skilton 1962, page 118

Llyn Cwellyn is passed on the road from Beddgelert to Caernarvon. Towne took his view from the high ground to the west of the road, above the bridge over the Afon Gwyrfai. The mountain on the left of the drawing is Mynydd Mawr and the steep cliff rising from the water is Carn Cwm Bychan, the crown of which is known as Castell Cidwm (the wolf's castle), the legendary stronghold of a robber chief. The hills to the right of Llyn Cwellyn are part of the north west range of the Snowdon massif.

ALEXANDER RUNCIMAN 1736–1785

18 *Ruined buildings, with distant hills seen across a wide valley*

Pencil, pen and ink, and watercolour, 5⅜ × 8⅞ inches
Provenance: The Hon. Lady Inglis

This and the following two landscape drawings date from the years 1766 to 1771, when the artist was a member of the Fuseli circle in Rome.

19 *A tree at the edge of a lake, with a house on the far shore*

Grey wash and watercolour, 7⅝ × 5¾ inches
Signed with a monogram
On the back: a slight sketch in red chalk of rococco forms, possibly plasterwork
Provenance: The Hon. Lady Inglis

See note on catalogue number 18.

20 *A temple perched on a rocky outcrop, seen across a lake*

Grey wash and watercolour, 5⅜ × 7½ inches
Signed with a monogram
On the back: a slight sketch in red chalk of serpentine forms
Provenance: The Hon. Lady Inglis

See note on catalogue number 18.

ANGELICA KAUFFMANN, R.A.   1741–1807

21   *Paulus Aemilianus with his family*   *Illustrated*

Pen and brown ink, with brown and grey washes, heightened with white, $8\frac{7}{8} \times 11\frac{5}{8}$ inches

Paulus Aemilianus was the father of the great Roman general Scipio Africanus, shown here as a boy about to try on a helmet.

JOHN HENRY FUSELI, R.A.   1741–1825

22   *A sheet with three figure studies: a young man in Renaissance costume with a plumed hat slung across his shoulders; a nude man sitting cross-legged on a chair; and a young girl in a diaphanous dress with a ruched collar*

Pen and brown ink, $7 \times 7\frac{7}{8}$ inches
Inscribed 'The Painter / however / seems / to have . . .'
On the back: two studies in pen and ink. The first, which is slight, is of women on a stage, or perhaps on the steps of a temple; the second is of a nude man in a similar pose to the seated figure on the front, but traced through in reverse and with features which appear more heroic, less satanic
Provenance: R.S. Timewell

BENJAMIN WEST, P.R.A.   1738–1820

23   *A party of skaters on a lake below a wooded bluff*

Pen and grey ink, with watercolour, $4\frac{7}{8} \times 5\frac{1}{2}$ inches
On the back: a slight pencil sketch of skaters
Provenance: the Smythe and Fowler families

A similar sketch, in black chalk, is in the Pierpont Morgan Library, New York.

THOMAS STOTHARD, R.A.   1755–1834

24   *A design for engraved tickets to a York festival concert*

Pen and ink, with watercolour, $4\frac{1}{8} \times 5\frac{1}{8}$ inches

According to a note on the page of the album in which this drawing was preserved, the artist received 10 guineas for his design.

FRANCOIS LOUIS THOMAS FRANCIA   1772–1839

25   *A windmill on the banks of a river by moonlight*

Watercolour, $2\frac{5}{8} \times 9\frac{1}{2}$ inches
Signed and dated 1801
Provenance : Walter Hetherington

26   *Shipping off a rocky headland*

Pencil and watercolour, $3\frac{1}{8} \times 6\frac{5}{8}$ inches
Signed

A small watercolour by Thomas Girtin of the same headland, without shipping, belonged to L. G. Duke and is now in another private collection.

27   *Soldiers guarding a mountain pass*   *Illustrated*

Pen and ink, with watercolour, $15\frac{1}{2} \times 12\frac{3}{8}$ inches
Signed and dated 1824
Provenance : R. J. Buck

JULIUS CAESAR IBBETSON   1759–1817

28   *Carrying home a faggot in winter : a cottager with children and a dog*

Pencil, pen and grey ink, and watercolour, $5\frac{5}{8} \times 4\frac{7}{8}$ inches

THOMAS ROWLANDSON   1756–1827

29   *Pigs*

Pencil, pen and ink, and watercolour, 5 × 6⅜ inches
Provenance: Joseph Grego

30   *Hengar House at St. Tudy, near Bodmin, Cornwall*   *Illustrated*

Pen and ink, with watercolour, 8 × 10¾ inches
Inscribed in pencil on the back 'Hengar House the seat of Mathw. Michell Esqr., Cornwall'
Literature: Dr. John Hayes, 'Rowlandson watercolours and drawings', Phaidon 1972,
page 20, illustrated page 19; Bernard Falk, 'Thomas Rowlandson, his life and art',
Hutchinson, pages 119 to 121, illustrated facing page 28

The banker Mathew Michell was a close friend of Rowlandson, many of whose drawings of
the Cornish landscape and villages were made on his visits to Hengar. The house was
destroyed by fire in 1904.

SAMUEL HOWITT   1756–1822

31   *Hudswell Scar in Swaledale, near Richmond, Yorkshire*

Pencil, pen and ink, and watercolour, 5⅜ × 7⅝ inches
Signed. Inscribed with the title on the original mount

HENRY WILLIAM BUNBURY   1750–1811

32   *A soiree*

Pen and ink, with watercolour, 10 × 15¾ inches

JOSHUA CRISTALL   1767–1847

33   *Two ladies with exotic head-dresses*

Pen and brown ink, with brown wash, heightened with white, $4\frac{1}{8} \times 2\frac{3}{4}$ inches
Signed

Cristall entered the Royal Academy School in 1792 under James Barry. This early drawing, however, appears to owe more to Fuseli, who succeeded Barry as Professor of Painting in 1799.

34   *Four consecutive pages from a sketchbook used in the Scottish Highlands in 1818*   *Illustrated*

A)   A mountain pass
        Pen and ink, with watercolour, $7\frac{1}{4} \times 6\frac{1}{8}$ inches
        Dated 1818

B)   Ben More
        Pencil, with pen and brown and blue inks, on two pages, $7\frac{1}{4} \times 12\frac{1}{4}$ inches
        Signed, inscribed 'Ben More, North Britain', and dated 1818

C)   A mountain landscape seen from below the tree-line
        Pencil, $7\frac{1}{4} \times 6\frac{1}{8}$ inches

35   *A woman in a brown dress, seen from the back*

Pencil and watercolour, $8\frac{3}{4} \times 5\frac{1}{8}$ inches
Faintly signed with initials in a reddish ink, and inscribed in pencil 'Bristol Life . . .'

The inscription suggests that Cristall may have attended a life class at Bristol, probably sometime between 1822 and 1841 when he was living in Herefordshire.

ROBERT HILLS   1769–1844

36   *A donkey*

Pencil and watercolour on fawn paper, $4\frac{1}{2} \times 2\frac{3}{4}$ inches

37   *A farmyard*

Pencil and watercolour, $3\frac{1}{8} \times 4\frac{5}{8}$ inches

GEORGE CHINNERY   1774–1852

38   *The banks of an Indian river, with the dome of a temple seen above*
trees   *Illustrated*

Pencil and watercolour, $4\frac{3}{4} \times 6\frac{1}{4}$ inches
On the back: a sketch in pencil and watercolour of an Indian temple, with tall columns
flanking the steps; and a fragment of a similar sketch
Provenance: Dr. Thomas Boswall Watson, Chinnery's doctor in Macao, and then by
descent to his great-grandson Major A. J. S. Watson

39   *Indian soldiers resting beside a ruined temple*

Pen and ink, with watercolour, $5\frac{1}{8} \times 5$ inches
Provenance: as for catalogue number 38

40   *Off He-'Ang Shan, with tanka boats on the shore*   *Illustrated*

Pencil, pen and ink, and watercolour, $4\frac{1}{4} \times 5\frac{5}{8}$ inches
Inscribed in pencil on the back and numbered 77
Provenance: as for catalogue number 38

CORNELIUS VARLEY 1781–1873

41 *Loading a sailing barge, grounded at low tide*

Pencil and watercolour, 15¼ × 14 inches
Signed, inscribed 'In Pt. Gc. Te.', and dated September 12, 1823

The inscription denotes that the drawing was made with the aid of a Patent Graphic Telescope, a form of camera obscura invented by the artist and patented in 1811.

JOHN VARLEY 1778–1842

42 *A view across London from Porchester Terrace, Bayswater*

Pencil and watercolour, 9 × 12¼ inches
Signed, inscribed 'Study from Nature', and dated 1831

By 1830 Varley's friend and former pupil John Linnell had built himself a grand house in Porchester Terrace, to which Varley was no doubt a frequent visitor.

WILLIAM HENRY HUNT 1790–1864

43 *The angler's breakfast* *Illustrated*

Pencil, pen and ink, and watercolour, 6⅞ × 8 inches
Signed. Inscribed in pencil on the back 'Sketch of William Prior Esqr. by W. Hunt. (Taken in his room where he lived at the Brewery)'

William Prior, of Middleton Square, Islington, was a patron of English watercolour painters, notably Hunt and de Wint, and was also a friend of the poet Keats.

JOHN SELL COTMAN   1782–1842

44   *The gateway at Helmsley Castle, Yorkshire, with a goat beneath the arch*

Pencil and watercolour, 7⅝ × 7 inches
Provenance: Sir Michael Sadler
Literature: Sydney D. Kitson, 'The life of John Sell Cotman', Faber and Faber 1937, page 54

This sketch dates from Cotman's first visit to Yorkshire in 1803, when he stayed with the Cholmeleys at Brandsby Hall, a few miles from Helmsley.

45   *Mousehold Heath, Norwich*

Oil on millboard, 7⅜ × 10⅛ inches
Provenance: The Rev. James Bulwer and Henry A. Bulwer, of Vancouver, his great-nephew

46   *A clump of trees on the banks of a river*   *Illustrated*

Watercolour, 5 × 9½ inches
Provenance: Dawson Turner

Painted about 1807. This drawing was laid on a two-ply card, on the bottom layer of which was found an earlier unfinished Cotman drawing in pencil and watercolour. The subject of this is an old building, with an oriel window, converted for use as a barn. The paper is watermarked 1798 and is inscribed on the back, referring to the watercolour here exhibited, 'No. 53 River Scene & Group of Trees. J. S. Cotman. Dawson Turner's Folio'.

JOHN SELL COTMAN   1782–1842

47   *Cley church, Norfolk*   *Illustrated*

Pencil and brown wash, $6\frac{7}{8} \times 10\frac{1}{2}$ inches
Signed and dated 1818. Inscribed with the title on the back

Engraved by W. Deeble for 'Excursions through Norfolk', volume 2, published 1819, the plate dated October 1st, 1818

48   *Middleton Tower, near King's Lynn, Norfolk*

Pencil and brown wash, $8\frac{5}{8} \times 7$ inches
Signed and dated 1818
Engraved by E. Roberts for 'Excursions through Norfolk', volume 2, published 1819, the plate dated September 1st, 1818

49   *A lake in a park, with swans on the water and groups of strollers on the shore*

Pencil, with touches of white and yellowish bodycolour, on fawn paper, $5\frac{1}{8} \times 7\frac{3}{4}$ inches
Inscribed on the back in pencil by the artist with notes on the colours and tones

A watercolour of this composition, dateable to about 1835, is in a private collection.

JOSEPH MALLORD WILLIAM TURNER, R.A.
1775–1851

50   *A ship amid icebergs: a study for a vignette*   *Illustrated*

Pencil and watercolour, $7 \times 5\frac{1}{2}$ inches
Provenance: J. E. Taylor
Exhibited: 'Watercolour drawings by J. M. W. Turner, R.A.', Agnew's 1913, catalogue
number 107
Literature: Sir Walter Armstrong, 'Turner', 1902, page 258

Andrew Wilton has suggested that this study belongs with the small group of paintings and
drawings which were inspired by Turner's reading of Thomas Beale's 'The Natural
History of the Sperm Whale', published in 1839. Of the whaling subjects exhibited by
Turner at the Royal Academy – two in 1845 and the two following year – three made
reference in their titles to Beale's Voyage. The vignette was the form favoured by Turner
for book illustration, and on the evidence of this drawing it is possible that he may have
contemplated a set of drawings to be engraved for an edition of Beale's work.

SAMUEL PROUT   1783–1852

51   *A ruined abbey in France used as a coach yard and hay shed*

Pencil, pen and ink, and watercolour, $2\frac{7}{8} \times 4\frac{1}{8}$ inches

52   *Old buildings round a harbour in Northern France*

Pencil, pen and ink, and watercolour, $2\frac{7}{8} \times 4\frac{1}{8}$ inches

JOHN CONSTABLE, R.A.   1776–1837

53   *Landscape with a stormy sky: possibly a view over London from*
Hampstead Heath   *Illustrated*

Watercolour, 4⅜ × 5¼ inches
On the back: a slight pencil study of Waterloo Bridge
Provenance: Gilbert Davis
Exhibited: 'Three centuries of British watercolours and drawings', Arts Council 1951,
catalogue number 45; 'John Constable', Guildhall Art Gallery 1952, catalogue number 70

The pencil study, unfortunately much disfigured, represents perhaps the seminal idea for
Constable's painting 'Waterloo Bridge, from Whitehall Stairs, June 18th, 1817', exhibited at the Royal Academy in 1832. The ceremonial opening of Waterloo Bridge by the
Prince Regent, which Constable probably witnessed, was a subject on which he worked at
intervals from 1819, the year in which he took a house at Hampstead for the first time.

WILLIAM ROXBY BEVERLEY   1811–1889

54   *Storm clouds over the sea*

Watercolour, 3¼ × 7½ inches

RICHARD PARKES BONINGTON   1802–1828

55   *Venice: ships moored on the lagoon*

Pencil, 4¼ × 5½ inches
Inscribed 'Venice' in pencil and numbered 76 faintly in ink

56   *A boat beached near a fisherman's cottage on the shore of an estuary*

Pencil and blue wash, heightened with white, on grey paper, 2⅛ × 6⅛ inches
Provenance: L. G. Duke

This small sketch, for which Dr. Marion Spencer has suggested a date of 1826, is closely
related both in technique and medium to the slightly larger 'Scene in Normandy',
formerly owned by Lord Kinnaird and now in the collection of the Sydney Art Gallery.

THOMAS SHOTTER BOYS   1803–1874

57   *A distant view of Oxford*   *Illustrated*

Pencil and watercolour, with touches of white, $11\frac{1}{2} \times 16\frac{1}{4}$ inches

The artist exhibited Oxford subjects in 1864 and 1866, but this drawing appears to be more consistent with his sketching style of an earlier period. In particular the handling of the architecture recalls vintage Boys of the 'thirties.

58   *Whitstable Bay, Kent*

Watercolour, $5\frac{1}{4} \times 10\frac{1}{2}$ inches
Provenance: Henry Browne Hagreen, who bought the drawing at the sale of the artist's effects after his death in St. John's Wood

59   *Open landscape with distant farm amid trees*

Pencil and watercolour, $4\frac{1}{2} \times 6\frac{3}{4}$ inches
Inscribed 'Sheepshearing'

60   *Trees in a park*

Watercolour, $3\frac{3}{8} \times 5$ inches

DAVID COX 1783–1859

61 *A cottage near Beckenham, Kent*

Watercolour, $5\frac{5}{8} \times 10\frac{3}{8}$ inches
Inscribed with the title on the back
Provenance: Walter Hetherington

62 *Near Beddgelert, North Wales*

Black chalk and watercolour, $9 \times 11\frac{1}{4}$ inches
On paper watermarked 'J. Whatman 1819'
Inscribed with the title on the back

63 *Cows and calves in a byre*   *Illustrated*

Black chalk and watercolour, $9\frac{1}{8} \times 13\frac{7}{8}$ inches
Signed and dated 1843

64 *The Thames at Fulham*

Pencil and watercolour, $5\frac{5}{8} \times 8\frac{1}{4}$ inches

Probably painted in the late 1820's after Cox's return to London from Hereford. The drawing may be compared with the view across Battersea fields exhibited in 'David Cox drawings and paintings' at this gallery in 1976, catalogue number 19, with illustration.

JOHN LINNELL   1792–1882

65   *A forest path flanked by bare beech trees*

Black chalk and watercolour, with touches of bodycolour, on blue paper, $10\frac{5}{8} \times 8\frac{1}{4}$ inches

66   *A shepherd boy piping*   *Illustrated*

Pencil and watercolour, with touches of bodycolour, $10\frac{3}{8} \times 8\frac{1}{2}$ inches
Signed and inscribed 'Shoreham'

Probably drawn in 1829, when Linnell visited Shoreham with George Richmond. It is a study for the painting 'The farmer's boy', exhibited at the Royal Academy in 1830 and now in the collection of the Museum of Fine Arts, Virginia. Another more elaborate study of the shepherd boy playing a recorder was shown in the loan exhibition of works by John Linnell and his circle at Colnaghi's in 1973. It was illustrated as the frontispiece to the catalogue.

SIR DAVID WILKIE, R.A.   1785–1841

67   *A sheepdog with pet rabbits*   *Illustrated*

Oil on panel, 5⅜ × 5¾ inches
Provenance: Sir William Knighton, Bart., Nelson Matcham, G.W.E. Jeffreys

Wilkie made use of this study when painting his 'Sheepwashing', which was exhibited at the British Institution in 1817 and is now in the collection of the National Gallery of Scotland.

68   *A King Charles spaniel*   *Illustrated*

Pencil, pen and ink, with brown wash, heightened with white and touches of red, on light fawn paper, 9⅝ × 7⅞ inches
Signed and dated 1835
Provenance: J. M. Teesdale

The drawing is a study for the dog in the painting 'The first ear-ring', exhibited at the Royal Academy in 1835.

JOHN FREDERICK LEWIS, R.A.   1805–1876

69   *The back of the Squirrel Inn at Winkfield, near Windsor, Berkshire*

Illustrated

Oil on millboard, $5\frac{3}{8} \times 8\frac{1}{4}$ inches

A letter attached to the back of the sketch from the artist's brother Charles to Francis Robinson says: 'I have great pleasure in presenting to you this little oil sketch by my brother John F. Lewis, A.R.A. The subject is the back of the Squirrel Inn, Winkfield, near Windsor. It was painted about the year 1826'.

Early in his career Lewis was commissioned by George IV to paint the deer at Windsor and other sporting subjects, and he may have visited the Squirrel Inn when sketching in the Great Park.

70   *A Highland crofter*

Watercolour, with touches of bodycolour, $7\frac{3}{4} \times 11\frac{1}{8}$ inches

This drawing dates from Lewis's visit to the Scottish Highlands in 1830.

FREDERICK JOHN SKILL   1824–1881

71   *A grey pony grazing in a lane*

Pencil and watercolour, $3\frac{1}{2} \times 2\frac{7}{8}$ inches
Signed

GEORGE RICHMOND, R.A.   1809–1896

72   *A man carrying a baby through a Gothic arch*

Pencil and watercolour, 5×3 inches
Provenance: The Rev. Canon Richmond, the artist's eldest son; and then by descent to Mrs. Miriam Hartley, the artist's great-great-granddaughter

JOHN MARTIN   1789–1854

73 *Kensington Gardens*   *Illustrated*

Pencil and watercolour, 9¾ × 7 inches
Inscribed in ink on the back 'Kensington Gardens. Martin'
Exhibited: 'John Martin loan exhibition', Hazlitt, Gooden & Fox 1975, catalogue number
28, illustrated plate 28

74 *A distant city with classical buildings seen across a lake*

Pencil, with brown and blue washes, 4¾ × 7¾ inches
Provenance: Palser Gallery, 1847

JAMES HOLLAND   1800–1870

75 *Bathing huts on the beach at Eastbourne*

Pencil and watercolour, heightened with white, 3⅞ × 6 inches
Signed with a monogram, inscribed '12.40 S.W.', and dated 9 September, '61
On the back: a cloud study in pencil and watercolour

JAMES SMETHAM   1821–1889

76 *The ebb tide: children playing with a toy boat in a sandy pool*

Pen and ink, with watercolour, 2½ × 5¼ inches
Signed
Provenance: Dennis Smetham

WILLIAM COLLINS, R.A.   1788–1847

77   *Going to school*

Pencil, with black and coloured chalks, $8\frac{1}{8} \times 6\frac{1}{8}$ inches
Provenance: The Earl of Northbrook, Mrs. A. H. Piper

78   *Two children examining a bird's egg*   *Illustrated*

Pen and ink, with watercolour and bodycolour, on light grey paper, $8\frac{3}{4} \times 7\frac{7}{8}$ inches
Inscribed on the original mount 'Study for bird-nesting'
Provenance: as for catalogue number 77

79   *A boy wearing a smock and a fur cap*

Pencil and watercolour on light pink paper, $8\frac{3}{8} \times 5\frac{5}{8}$ inches
Provenance: as for catalogue number 77

80   *A boy with a boathook*

Pencil and watercolour on light fawn paper, $10\frac{1}{4} \times 9\frac{1}{8}$ inches
Provenance: as for catalogue number 77

The drawing is a study for the fisherboy in 'The prawn catchers', which Collins exhibited at the Royal Academy in 1828. The painting was bought by Robert Vernon and is now in the collection of the Tate Gallery.

FREDERICK WILLIAM WATTS   1800–1870

81   *Haymakers resting*

Oil on millboard, $4\frac{1}{2} \times 6\frac{3}{4}$ inches

Comparable small studies in oil of haymaking scenes are in the collection of the Tate Gallery.

JOHN PHILLIP, R.A.   1817–1867

82   *Mountain goats*   *Illustrated*

Oil on millboard, $10\frac{3}{4} \times 8\frac{5}{8}$ inches

GEORGE HEMING MASON, A.R.A.   1818–1872

83   *A view of the Roman Campagna, with a thatched shelter for horses*

Oil on millboard, $3\frac{3}{4} \times 13\frac{7}{8}$ inches

When living in Rome from 1844 to 1858, Mason was a prominent member of the group of English and Italian artists which later – after Mason's death – became known as the Etruscan school.

FRANCIS DANBY, A.R.A.   1793–1861

84   *Evening landscape, with a castle overlooking a lake*

Oil on panel, $5\frac{1}{8} \times 8\frac{3}{4}$ inches

85   *View from the drawing room window of the artist's house at Exmouth*   *Illustrated*

Oil on paper, laid on card, $9\frac{3}{4} \times 5\frac{5}{8}$ inches

Danby moved from Lewisham to Exmouth in 1847. He was a passionate amateur boat builder, so the move may have been prompted as much by the call of the sea and the prospect of building and sailing his own boats as by any concern for his interests as a painter. For the first nine years at Exmouth he lived at Rill Cottage, the exact site of which is not known. Later, in the hope of making a better studio for himself, he removed to Shell House, overlooking the estuary, where he lived until his death.

86   *Boat building*

Oil on paper, laid on card, $5 \times 7\frac{1}{2}$ inches

From his second Exmouth home Danby's boat building could be given full rein on the dunes in front of the house. At least one of his boats was evidently of some tonnage, because it had a cabin below decks. Not surprisingly, these activities absorbed time and energy which might more profitably have been spent in painting. An amusing contemporary impression of Danby as a 'boat builder who sometimes painted' is quoted by Eric Adams in 'Francis Danby: varieties of poetic landscape', Yale University Press 1973, page 112.

JOHN EDWARD BRETT, A.R.A.   1830–1902

87   *Seascape*

Oil on panel, $5 \times 8\frac{1}{2}$ inches
Signed

Like Danby, Brett was an enthusiastic yachtsman. An entry in Beatrix Potter's diary for 1884 records that Brett was 'sailing about the west coast of Scotland in his yacht in the summer, making oil sketches which he uses for the colour in his pictures which he paints in the winter months, chiefly from memory'.

WILLIAM JAMES MULLER   1812–1845

88   *Still life with jugs and baskets*   *Illustrated*

Pencil and watercolour, $12\frac{3}{8} \times 9\frac{3}{8}$ inches

89   *Hampstead Heath*

Black chalk and watercolour, with touches of white, on fawn paper, $4\frac{3}{4} \times 7\frac{3}{8}$ inches
Provenance: Alfred Downing Fripp

A signed note by Fripp, stuck to the original backboard, records that 'This sketch by
William Muller was made at Clipstone St. Academy Friday evening sketching society, of
which he was a member with Dodgson, Dighton, Baxter, Poole, Bentley, Jenkins, Ed.
Duncan, F. Goodall, myself and others, and given to me in exchange. It was done in about
ten minutes, his second on the same evening, in the winter of 1843 or 44, and has never
been out of my possession'.

90   *Inside a house in Asia Minor*

Pencil and watercolour, $13 \times 18\frac{3}{8}$ inches

91   *Ruins of a mausoleum in a wood, Lycia*

Pencil and watercolour, $8\frac{7}{8} \times 14\frac{3}{4}$ inches
On the back: a slight, unrelated pencil sketch of buildings amid trees

92   *Vines on the banks of a river near Masry, Asia Minor*

Watercolour, 20×13 inches, with arched top
Signed with initials, inscribed with the title and dated 1844, February 10 below the mount

PETER DE WINT   1784-1849

93   *A cottage seen through trees*

Oil on millboard, $12\frac{3}{4} \times 12$ inches
Provenance: J. and W. Vokins, Major K. L. G. Dixon

94   *Studies of a greyhound*   *Illustrated*

Black and white chalks on fawn paper, $10\frac{3}{8} \times 14$ inches
Provenance: Miss Sarah Brooks, whose grandmother, Mrs. Boover Brooks, was de Wint's
aunt; and then by descent to Mrs. A. G. Dawes

95   *Dock and other wild plants*

Watercolour, $5\frac{5}{8} \times 7\frac{1}{8}$ inches
Provenance: as for catalogue number 94

96   *Loading a haywain*

Watercolour, $1\frac{7}{8} \times 3\frac{3}{8}$ inches
Provenance: as for catalogue number 94

JOHN MIDDLETON   1827–1856

97   *A fallen tree*   *Illustrated*

Watercolour, $8\frac{3}{8} \times 11\frac{3}{4}$ inches

This drawing relates closely in subject matter, treatment and palette to a watercolour of the park at Hatfield, Hertfordshire, dated 1848, which is in a private collection.

EDWARD DUNCAN   1803–1882

98   *Shipping off a harbour mouth*

Pencil and watercolour, $6\frac{3}{4} \times 9\frac{7}{8}$ inches
Signed. Bears studio stamp

EDWARD LEAR   1812–1888

99   *The Lake of Butrinto, near the coast of Albania, opposite Corfu*

Illustrated

Pen and ink, with watercolour, $8\frac{3}{4} \times 12\frac{1}{4}$ inches
Inscribed with notes and dated 7 January, 1857
Provenance: R. J. Berkeley

Lear lived on the island of Corfu from 1855 until his long-projected departure for Jerusalem in March 1858. From Corfu he made many sketching forays across the narrow sound into Albania.

HERCULES BRABAZON BRABAZON   1821–1906

100   *The Salute, Venice*

Pencil and watercolour, with touches of bodycolour, on light fawn paper, $4\frac{7}{8} \times 6\frac{5}{8}$ inches
Signed with initials. Inscribed with the title on the back and numbered 26
Exhibited: 'Watercolours and pastels by the late Hercules Brabazon Brabazon', Goupil Gallery 1906, catalogue number C53

JOHN RUSKIN   1819–1900

101 *Lake Lugano*   *Illustrated*

Watercolour, with touches of bodycolour, on light blue paper, $9\frac{5}{8} \times 12$ inches
Provenance: The Rev. Richard St. John Tyrrwhitt

Tyrrwhitt (1827–1895) was an admirer of Ruskin, in whose favour he withdrew his
candidature for the Slade Professorship of Fine Arts in 1869. He was the author of
'Christian Art and Symbolism, with hints on the study of Landscape', 1872, for which
Ruskin wrote the preface. Tyrrwhitt was also an amateur artist and in his diary entry for
January 26th, 1885, Ruskin records having had the previous night 'a not unpleasant dream
of correcting some friend's, perhaps St. J. Tyrrwhitt's, mountain drawing into better
chiaroscuro with vigorous veto on his attempted remonstrances'.

Ruskin visited Lake Lugano on at least four occasions – in July 1844, May 1862, August
1869 and July 1870.

THOMAS COLLIER   1840–1891

102 *Landscape with stormy sky*

Pencil and watercolour, $6\frac{5}{8} \times 9\frac{3}{4}$ inches
Signed
Provenance: T. W. Bacon

103 *Meadow near Arundel, Sussex*

Pencil and watercolour, $3\frac{3}{4} \times 6\frac{5}{8}$ inches
Signed
Provenance: T. W. Bacon

104 *Whitby sands*

Pencil and watercolour, $3\frac{7}{8} \times 6$ inches
Signed, inscribed and dated 1877

JOSEPH CRAWHALL 1861–1913

105 *A dairymaid milking a black and white cow in a field*

Oil on panel, $5\frac{7}{8} \times 7\frac{7}{8}$ inches
Signed and dated '83
Provenance: William Young, Mrs. S. A. A. Norgaard
Exhibited: Laing Art Gallery, Newcastle upon Tyne, 1938
Literature: Adrian Bury, 'Joseph Crawhall – the man and the artist', Charles Skilton 1958, illustrated page 49

In this early work Crawhall appears to have taken his motif of the cow and the kneeling dairymaid from one of his father's woodcuts.

106 *A bay horse and a donkey in a stable*   *Illustrated*

Watercolour, with touches of bodycolour, on fine holland linen, $11\frac{1}{8} \times 12\frac{3}{8}$ inches
Provenance: J. E. Crawhall Wood, the artist's nephew; Adrian Bury
Literature: Adrian Bury, 'Joseph Crawhall – the man and the artist', Charles Skilton 1958, page 240

JOSEPH CRAWHALL   1861–1913

107 *L'enfant prodigue*   *Illustrated*

Watercolour and bodycolour on fine holland linen, 8 × 4¾ inches
Inscribed with the title in decorative lettering
Provenance: J. E. Crawhall Wood, the artist's nephew
Literature: Adrian Bury, 'Joseph Crawhall – the man and the artist', Charles Skilton 1958, page 230

Possibly a design for a theatre programme or a menu cover. The connection between the title and a game of French cricket played by children in a park is obscure.

JAMES ABBOT McNEILL WHISTLER, R.A.   1834–1903

108 *Nocturne*

Pen and brown ink, with brown wash, 1⅞ × 3⅝ inches
Signed in ink with butterfly device
Exhibited: 'Whistler – the graphic work: Amsterdam, Liverpool, London, Venice', shown in 1976 (the bi-centenary year of American Independence) at Agnew's, London, the Walker Art Gallery, Liverpool, and the City Art Gallery, Glasgow, catalogue number 85

In her catalogue entry for the above exhibition, Mrs Margaret MacDonald writes, 'The signature dates the drawing in the early eighties. It was certainly not drawn in Venice, but the drawing reflects Whistler's concern with the problems involved in drawing with pen, as with etched lines, the effects of lights at night. It relates closely to his Venice etchings, like the "Nocturne", which was then being printed, but not otherwise to his paintings or graphic work of the eighties'.

AUBREY BEARDSLEY

AUBREY VINCENT BEARDSLEY 1872–1898

109 *A Christmas card* *Illustrated*

Pen and black ink, $9\frac{5}{8} \times 6\frac{1}{8}$ inches
Signed
Provenance: R. A. Walker
Exhibited: 'Loan exhibition of drawings by Aubrey Beardsley', Tate Gallery, November 1923 to March 1924, and then at the Whitworth Institute, Manchester, and the City Art Gallery, Leeds, catalogue number 40

The drawing was commissioned by Leonard Smithers for the first issue of 'The Savoy'. A photo-mechanical reproduction of it was inserted loose in each copy as a Christmas card. This attempt to appeal to the Christmas market failed, however, because publication of 'The Savoy' was delayed and the first issue did not appear until January 1896. For this rare interpretation of a religious theme, Beardsley appears to have turned for inspiration to the early Italian masters.

JESSIE MARION KING 1875–1949

110 *A young woman sketching, possibly a self-portrait*

Pencil and watercolour, $8\frac{3}{4} \times 7\frac{1}{4}$ inches
Provenance: Miss Merle Taylor, the artist's daughter

CHRISTOPHER RICHARD WYNNE NEVINSON, A.R.A.
1889–1946

111 *Column on the march*   *Illustrated*

Black chalk and watercolour, heightened with bodycolour, $7\frac{3}{8} \times 8\frac{3}{4}$ inches

As a signatory to the Futurist Manifesto, published in June 1914 by the Italian poet Marinetti, Nevinson clearly did not at that time find the prospect of war abhorrent. On the eve of the holocaust, this group of avant-garde artists was ready to welcome the machinery and instruments of war as a cleansing force, symbols of a virile new age of speed, efficiency and destruction. For Nevinson, at least, such intellectual posturing ended abruptly when he was posted to Flanders as an ambulance driver and saw for himself the horrors of the trenches. He remained true, however, to the techniques of futurist painting, the angular, fragmented images and the mechanical ryhthms, reminiscent of superimposed cine frames.

'I have tried', he said in an interview early in 1915, 'to express the emotion produced by the apparent ugliness and dullness of modern warfare. The futurist technique is the only possible medium to express the crudeness, violence and brutality of the emotions seen and felt on the battle fields . . . Modern art needs not beauty, or restraint, but vitality'.

This drawing is closely related to the 1915 oil painting of the same title, in the collection of L. J. Cadbury. It is not certain, however, whether the drawing is a study for the oil, or a smaller and later version of the composition. The oil, which measures $24 \times 29\frac{1}{2}$ inches, was illustrated in colour as the frontispiece to 'Modern war: paintings by C. R. W. Nevinson', Grant Richards 1917.

ROBERT POLHILL BEVAN   1865–1925

112   *Breton girls*

Black chalk and watercolour, $4\frac{3}{4} \times 7\frac{5}{8}$ inches
Signed
Provenance: Mrs. Rosemary Peto

This drawing may date from the artist's first visit to Brittany in 1891.

113   *Sabot makers, Brittany*   *Illustrated*

Black and coloured chalks, with wash, $9\frac{7}{8} \times 13\frac{1}{2}$ inches
Bears the studio stamp on the bottom right margin, below the mount
Provenance: Philip Stobo
Exhibited: 'Robert Bevan', Arts Council of Great Britain 1956, catalogue number 43
Literature: R. A. Bevan, 'Robert Bevan, a memoir by his son', Studio Vista 1965,
illustrated plate 7

Bevan was again in Brittany in 1893 and 1894, staying at the Villa Julia in Pont Aven,
where he met and came greatly to admire Paul Gauguin. Many of Bevan's compositions at
this period show traditional Breton craftsmen at work. Sabot making, one of his favourite
subjects, inspired a number of drawings and a lithograph.

PHILIP WILSON STEER   1860–1942

114   *Alum Bay, Isle of Wight*

Watercolour, $9\frac{1}{2} \times 13\frac{1}{2}$ inches
Provenance: R. J. Berkeley

Painted in 1919.

Lund Humphries